BONNIE N. COLLIDE
Nine to Five

by Monica Gallagher

Lipstick Press
www.eatyourlipstick.com
lipstickisspress@gmail.com
Baltimore, MD, USA

First Edition: December 2015
Printed in Canada
ISBN 978-0-9794589-3-4

INTRODUCTION
by Greg Lockard

Monica Gallagher is amazing.

This collection of Bonnie N. Collide, Nine to Five represents over 7 YEARS of weekly comic strip work. That level of commitment is impressive and is multiplied by the fact that she accomplished this while maintaining her own 9-to-5 day-job, publishing two full-length original graphic novels, numerous comic books, attending countless comic conventions, book signings and even starting her own podcast... and playing roller derby in her "spare" time, too!

Artist-rendered assumption of what Greg would look like as a werewolf

If you haven't read the story of Bonnie N. Collide, I am excited for you to discover a wonderful and hilarious treat. Our hero, Bonnie, balances her work-life and roller derby-life by completely ignoring the lines that divide the two. Bonnie is surrounded by the amazing women of derby and also by a group of co-workers both super-real and lovably-freaky. It's a workplace sit-com with genius hints of the absurd--Bonnie in constant derby gear and the hairiest curveball: a werewolf co-worker named "Herb."

WHAT?! The character is introduced so matter-of-factly, too. He's always a werewolf, he's always in the office and his co-workers have a normal amount of hesistence around his intimidating personality... but they never question his existence. It's brilliant. Actually, it's beyond brilliant but I can only repeat:

Monica Gallagher is amazing.

What I love about Monica's stories is the Jim Henson-like approach to her care and creation of character. Which is the highest of compliments direct from my felt-covered heart: we're all weirdos, freaks and monsters and that's what bonds us together.

I'm lucky to call Monica a friend. She laughs a lot, she's kind and she's very humble-- which is why I am happy to introduce this volume by a creative force-of-nature while shouting from the rooftops:

Monica Gallagher is amazing.

Bonnie N. Collide	Mimi Madness	Stuart	Herb	Sherry & Barb	Hattie Hellfire
Rollergirl with a day job. Doin' it the best she can, nine to five.	Bonnie's best friend. Too busy for anybody's nonsense.	Bonnie's boyfriend, diligently trying to chip away to get to the REAL Bonnie.	Office Boss and all-around dapper werewolf.	Gossipy officemates. Sun worshippers.	Terrifyingly friendly captain of the Hammerin' Harpies.

Fresh Meat Fran	Greg	Carl	Ted	Roomie Elisa	Roomie Cheryl
Newest edition to the roller derby league. Working on getting on a team.	Another office gossip, specifically out to impress Carl.	Just a dude, working this job to get to his next bigger, better job.	Devoted husband of Arty-Choke Hold and derby widower confidant of Stuart.	Bonnie's roommate, who keeps forgetting what she looks like.	Stuart's roommate, who's madly in love with him.

Agro Amelia	Harold	Mouthpiece Molly	Albert	George	Henderson
That rollergirl who always kicks your ass. Fond of knocking down Fran.	Herb's husband and lover of dinner parties.	Pivot with an odd preference to wear her mouthguard 24/7.	One of a trio of Stuart's close buds - likes hot pants.	One of a trio of Stuart's close buds - thinks Bonnie is fun.	One of a trio of Stuart's close buds - always into the group dynamic.

Steve	Klatu Veronica	Tyrion Sinister	Lorelei Getmore	Violet Punch	Slam Quint
Has a crush on Cheryl and is a member of the Bigfoot Society.	Member of the Hammerin' Harpies and Coach of injured skaters.	Co-captain of the Sneering Sirens and Coach of fresh meat.	Captain of the Murderous Muses – the team Molly, Bonnie, and Mimi share.	New friend/crush of Fran's who plays for an out-of-state derby league.	New League Ref who (kind of) has a way with the ladies.

1 Meet Bonnie

MORNING COMMUTE TO WORK

COFFEE BREAK

THAT'S **MY** MOCHA NO-WHIP LATTE, BITCH! LOOK OUT!

WORK UNTIL FIVE O'CLOCK

GIVE ME MY DOCUMENT ALREADY!!

RUN ERRANDS

OUTTA THE WAY OF THE CHIPS!

AFTER-WORK SOCIAL ACTIVITY

AHHH . . . DOWN TIME.

HEY PHIL

YEAH?

DID YOU EVER NOTICE THAT THERE'S A ROLLER GIRL WORKING HERE?

WHO, BONNIE? YEAH, OF COURSE. WHY?

I JUST NEVER NOTICED BEFORE

⧽PSH⧼ YEAH, RIGHT. NEXT, YOU'LL TELL ME YOU DIDN'T NOTICE HERB WAS A WEREWOLF

SOMEBODY CALL ME?

3

footer_nav text:

2 Meet Stuart

SO I THINK MY FAVORITE MOMENT WAS WHEN KATHY FROM SALES DECIDED IT WAS *HER* DANCE FLOOR...

...AND *ONLY* HER DANCE FLOOR...

OH!

OOF!

WATCH IT, JERK!

vvvROOM

BUMP

UM...

DEAR STUART, I'M SORRY I KNOCKED YOU ON YOUR ASS

DEAR STUART, I HAD FUN AT THE HOLIDAY PARTY!

EXCEPT THAT LAST PART, WHEN I KNOCKED YOU ON YOUR ASS

ARE YOU OKAY?

DEAR STUART, I HAVE ONE OF THOSE INFLATABLE ASS TIRE THINGIES IF YOU NEED IT

OR AN ICE PACK

I CAN'T TELL YOU HOW MANY ASS INJURIES I'VE HAD, SO I FEEL YOUR PAIN!

DEAR STUART, I HOPE I DIDN'T BREAK YOUR ASS THE OTHER NIGHT, BECAUSE I ASSUME THAT IT'S NICE.

HAPPY VALENTINE'S DAY! -- BONNIE.

GOT ANY FUN WEEKEND PLANS, BONNIE?

WORKPLACE ACCIDENTS SUCK!
SO REMEMBER:
• Coffee is hot
• Drives are sharp
• Microwaves are not toys

YEAH! I'M GOING TO GET UP EARLY TOMORROW, GET IN SOME PRACTICE SKATING, THEN DRIVE AN HOUR OUT TO THE ARENA TO HELP LAY THE ROLLER DERBY TRACK, THEN WARM-UP, THEN SKATE IN THE BOUT FOR FOUR HOURS, THEN HELP DISASSEMBLE THE TRACK, THEN GET CHANGED, THEN GO TO THE AFTER PARTY, AND THEN DANCE AND DRINK ALL NIGHT.

Y'KNOW, A TYPICAL SATURDAY. HOW ABOUT YOU?

OH ... I'M JUST GOING TO WATCH TV AND DRINK

UM ... MY TYPICAL SATURDAY

FIGHT

SORRY! I WAS SUPPOSED TO WASH THEM DURING THE LOST HOUR

YECCH, BONNIE, YOUR PADS REEK!

THE WHAT?

Y'KNOW, THE LOST HOUR. THE HOUR WE LOSE TO DAYLIGHT SAVINGS TIME.

SO ... WHY DIDN'T YOU WASH YOUR PADS?

⸢SIGH⸥ BECAUSE IF YOU FORGET TO FACTOR IN DAYLIGHT SAVINGS TIME, EVERYTHING YOU WERE SUPPOSED TO DO IN THE LOST HOUR GETS TAKEN AWAY FROM YOU.

THEN WHAT HAPPENS WHEN WE GAIN AN HOUR?

THAT'S THE MIRACLE HOUR, WHERE WE GET TO DO ANYTHING WE WANT WITHOUT CONSEQUENCES

SO WAIT ... DESPITE ALL THE RULES, YOU CAN STILL WASH YOUR PADS, RIGHT? ...

15

3 First Bout

OKAY, SO THERE'S REALLY ONLY **THREE THINGS** YOU HAVE TO REMEMBER ABOUT THE RULES OF FLAT-TRACK DERBY

(1) THERE ARE TWO TEAMS ON THE TRACK FORMING A PACK, MADE UP OF:

BLOCKERS

PIVOTS

(2) JAMMERS ARE THE POINT-SCORERS, AND THERE'S ONE FROM EACH TEAM. THEY SCORE POINTS BY GETTING THROUGH THE PACK.

(3) BLOCKING HAPPENS TO PREVENT THE OTHER TEAM'S JAMMER FROM SCORING, OR TO HELP **YOUR** JAMMER GET THROUGH.

SO WHAT HAPPENS WHEN THEY GET IN THE PENALTY BOX?

OH, THAT WHEN W DO THIS

BULLSHIT CALL!!

FO WHA FAFFENED FO FOUR FWEND?

I DON'T KNOW, I CAN'T FIND HIM . . .

I HOPE HE DIDN'T GET INTIMIDATED AND RUN OFF

FELL, FOMEFIMES FIFF WORLF IF HARD FOR FEEFLE FO UNDERFAND

YOU KNOW YOU CAN TAKE YOUR MOUTH-PIECE OUT NOW, RIGHT, MOLLY? BOUT'S OVER.

YOU KNOW YOU CAN TAKE YOUR *GEAR* OFF, RIGHT, BONNIE?

TOUCHÉ, MOLLY. TOUCHÉ.

WHIP IT

:SIGH:

REMEMBER: OPEN DOOR SLOWLY!

SOMEONE COULD BE ON THE OTHER SIDE!

:SIGH:

REMEMBER: COFFEE IS HOT!

:SIGH:

REMEMBER: DON'T FLUSH PAPER TOWELS IN THE TOILET!

SORRY BONNIE, IF YOU GIVE ME AN OPENING, I'M GONNA **HIT** YOU!

WELL, AT LEAST IN DERBY I'M TREATED LIKE AN ADULT!

PSST PSST

LUNCH TIME!

:SIGH: DO YOU EVER GET SICK OF NOT FITTING IN?

LUNCH TIME!

...OF NOT BEING "NORMAL"?

CRUNCH CRUNCH CRUNCH

WHENEVER I SEE WHAT'S CONSIDERED "NORMAL"...

I NEVER GET SICK OF **NOT** BEING THAT

DING!

TAG

WHUH?

YOU'RE IT

IT'S YOUR TURN TO INVITE ME TO *YOUR* THING!

WORK WORK WORK

DERBY DERBY DERBY

WORK WORK WORK WORK

DERBY DERBY DERBY

GAH!!

WHO ARE YOU AND WHAT ARE YOU DOING IN MY HOUSE??!

≶FLICK≶

HAVE I BEEN GONE *THAT* LONG?

27

4 Dating in Derby

ON YOUR LEFT! LOOK OUT!

OH YEAH... I ALWAYS FORGET THERE ARE PEOPLE OUT HERE TRAINING FOR SOMETHING *OTHER* THAN DERBY

ALTHOUGH I CAN'T FOR THE LIFE OF ME FIGURE OUT *WHY*...

ON YOUR LEF JOGGER! MOVE IT!!

...LET'S ASK HER.

BONNIE, HOW DO *YOU* KEEP MOTIVATED TO STAY IN SHAPE?

WOMEN WILL BEAT THE SHIT OUT OF ME IF I'M *NOT* IN SHAPE

OH... YOU MEAN, LIKE, OTHER WOMEN WILL BEAT YOU OUT FOR YOUR MAN'S ATTENTION?

NO, I MEAN WOMEN WILL **BEAT** THE **SHIT** OUT OF ME

OH! SO YOU HAVE A CONTROLLING GIRLFRIEND WHO INSISTS YOU SAY IN SHAPE?

NO.

I MEAN WOMEN WILL BEAT.

THE SHIT.

OUT OF.

ME.

I DON'T GET HER

THAT AWKWARD MOMENT WHEN YOU REALIZE YOU ORIGINALLY GAVE A CHARACTER A **TOTALLY** DIFFERENT TATTOO! YUP, THAT'S MIMI ROCKING AN ELEPHANT TATTOO ... WHICH LATER MORPHS INTO A PHOENIX ON HER UPPER LEFT ARM. :)

39

5 Fall Picnic

.. AAAAND HERE I DON'T EVEN PUT MIMI'S TATTOO IN AT ALL!

48

6 Fresh Meat Fran

50

51

KNOCK KNOCK

UH... YEAH?

CHERYL, CAN I TALK TO YOU FOR A SEC?

ARE YOU DECENT?

UM, SURE

COME ON IN!

SO LISTEN...

I HAVE A DATE WITH BONNIE THIS WEEKEND AND I WAS GOING TO INVITE HER *HERE*

SO I WAS WONDERING IF YOU COULD --

MAKE YOURSELF SCARCE

MAKE DINNER? SURE!

...OH

SORRY, I KNOW WE'VE NEVER TALKED ABOUT STUFF LIKE THIS BEFORE

I GUESS WE'VE BOTH HAD DRY SPELLS, HUH

NO, YEAH, TOTALLY - OF COURSE!

THE TIE ON THE DOORKNOB OR WHATEVER

SO YOU'RE OKAY WITH STAYING SOMEWHERE ELSE SATURDAY NIGHT?

SO YOU CAN HAVE SEX WITH BONNIE IN OUR APART-

ABSOLUTELY!

GREAT! THANKS, ROOMIE!

⦗SHUT⦘

I LOVE YOU

54

SOOO . . .

. . . YOU GONNA TELL ME HOW THE BIG DATE WENT?

BONNIE?

EARTH TO

EH?

FINE THEN, IF YOU WON'T SHARE, I'M GOING TO ASSUME IT WAS *HORRIBLE*.

HEY! I'M *SMILING*!

TOO LATE! HE SUCKS IN BED!

MIMI!

JEEZ, IT'S A GHOST TOWN IN HERE!

WHERE IS EVERYONE?

START OF SUMMER VACATION

JUNE

HOLIDAY TRIPS

JULY

ALL THE BIG WIGS TAKE THE MONTH OF AUGUST OFF, DON'T YOU KNOW THAT?

AUGUST

SO NOW WE CAN FINALLY GET BACK TO --

UH-UH

KIDS ARE BACK IN SCHOOL, TEACHER MEETINGS, SUPPLY SHOPPING . . .

YOU'RE DATING SOMEONE FROM *WORK?*

EW!

C'MON, BONNIE! I THOUGHT YOU'D BE BANGING SOME HOT *DERBY GUY* OR SOMETHING!

(OR DERBY GIRL)

AND HAVE SKATE SEX STORIES!

LOOK, STUART'S GREAT!

*STU*ART?

AND HE WORKS ON THE FOURTH FLOOR, SO IT'S NOT LIKE WE *REALLY* WORK TOGETHER

THE FOURTH FLOOR?!

I ALREADY WARNED HER IT WAS CREEPY UP THERE

HERB!

WAKE UP!

AAAH!

WHAT'S HAPPENING?

ARE WE BEING INVADED??

LOOK!!

LOOK AT THAT LEAF!

LEAF?

FALL IS HERE!!!

OKAY, I'VE BROUGHT ALL SORTS OF THINGS TO HELP PLAN YOUR PICNIC

RACE IDEAS, COSTUME PRIZES, GAMES . . . YOU NAME IT

SO . . .

WHICH WOULD YOU RATHER DO FIRST - PLAN THE PICNIC . . .

OR MAKE OUT?

WELL NOW I'VE FORGOTTEN ALL OF MY IDEAS

DECISION MADE!

SO DO YOU THINK THIS WILL BE BETTER OR WORSE THAN LAST YEAR?

CUBE CORP ANNUAL Fall Picnic

EQUALLY AS FRIGHTENING

WAIT . . .

I THINK I KNOW WHAT . . .

WHAT IS THIS

OH MY GOD, IT'S FINALLY HAPPENING

THEY'RE GONNA LET HERB FEED ON THE WORKFORCE

2012 HUNGER GAMES TEAM BUILD!

FORMER MEMBERS OF RED TEAM, YOU ARE NOW DISTRICT ONE!

WHO DOES THIS? WHO BASES A COMPANY FUNCTION ON A SERIES OF POPULAR BOOKS?

IT COULD'VE BEEN WORSE

WORSE THAN *KILLING* EACHOTHER FOR SURVIVAL??

ONLY IF YOU THINK MAKING US YOUR SEX SLAVES IS BETTER

WHAT ARE YOU, *THINKING* ABOUT IT?

MIGHT BE KIND OF COOL . . .

WELCOME EVERYONE!

SO IT LOOKS LIKE DISTRICT TWO IS IN THE LEAD

THEY HAD A SLIGHT MISSTEP IN THE THREE LEGGED RACE, BUT CRUSHED DISTRICT FIVE IN THE COPIER SLALOM

DAMNIT, SHERRY!

IN SECOND PLACE WE HAVE

ROAR

AAAIIIEEEEEEEEEE

AND WE HAVE AN UPSTART FOR FIRST PLACE!

TEAM HERB!

AND THE *WINNER* OF TEAM BUILD HUNGER GAMES ANNUAL FALL AWESOME IDEA BONNIE PICNIC IS . . .

TEAM HERB!

WHAT!

HE'S A TEAM OF *ONE!*

YEAH, HOW CAN AN *INDIVIDUAL* WIN A TEAM BUILD?

YOU GUYS ARE MISSING THE POINT!

HE *WOLFED OUT* AND ATTACKED EVERYONE!

YES, BUT NO ONE GOT HURT

HEY!

OKAY, NO ONE BUT *PHIL'S ANKLE* GOT HURT

SO BONNIE, WHO ARE YOU VOTING FOR?

FREEDOM!

WHICH PARTY DO YOU BELONG TO?

JUSTICE!

I'M GONNA GO IN THERE AND VOTE THE *CRAP* OUT OF THAT BALLOT!

VOTE

WOOOOO!

HIGH FIVES FOR LIBERTY!

VOTE

ELECTIONS ARE ALWAYS SO DRAMATIC

67

HA HA HA HA HA HA HA HA HA HA

YEAH, YEAH . . .

I KNEW ALL ALONG IT WAS JUST A BIG *JOKE*

NO ONE WAS *LESS* SCARED THAN ME

OKAY, I THINK THIS ABOUT DOES IT!

WHUMP

WHAT IS ALL THIS STUFF?

JUST MY ESSENTIALS

PJ'S TOOTHBRUSH

WORK CLOTHES

DERBY GEAR

WOW, I HAD NO IDEA WHAT YOU HAVE TO GO THROUGH JUST TO SPEND THE NIGHT

I REALLY APPRECIATE IT!

NAH, NO WORRIES

OH! AND CAN YOU SET YOUR ALARM FOR FOUR O'CLOCK?

7 Married to Derby

HEY BONNIE

YOU'RE HERE EARLY

HI HATTIE

YEAH, STILL WORKING OUT THE KINKS OF COMING HERE STRAIGHT FROM WORK WHEN I STAY OVER AT STUART'S

OOOH, SOUNDS SERIOUS

WELL, AS SERIOUS AS IT CAN BE --

FOR A GIRL ALREADY MARRIED TO *DERBY*

AM I MARRIED TO DERBY?

AT THIS POINT, PEOPLE EXPECTED YOU AND DERBY TO HAVE HAD KIDS BY NOW

MIMI, DO YOU THINK I'M *TOO* INTO DERBY?

I DON'T UNDERSTAND THE QUESTION

LIKE MY WHOLE LIFE IS WRAPPED UP IN DERBY AND I DON'T DO ANYTHING ELSE?

WELL YEAH ...

BUT YOU KIND OF *HAVE* TO BE THAT WAY ... TO BE IN DERBY

HOW DO YOU THINK PEOPLE IN **FOOTBALL** AND **BASEBALL** MANAGE TO HAVE LIVES?

PSHH ...

THOSE ARE JUST *SPORTS*

THIS IS DERBY!

SO BONNIE, DO YOU HAVE PLANS FOR THANKSGIVING?

WELL, I USUALLY TAG ALONG WITH ELISA OR MIMI

RIP!

WHY DON'T YOU COME OVER TO OUR HOUSE?

AMY'S A GREAT COOK AND I'M AN EVEN BETTER BARTENDER

SURE! THAT SOUNDS AWESOME

THANKS!

YOU CAN EVEN INVITE STUART, IF YOU LIKE

OHH ... IS THAT SOMETHING I SHOULD BE DOING, NOW THAT WE'RE HAVING SEX?

PAT PAT

WE'LL GET YOU USED TO THIS RELATIONSHIP STUFF IN NO TIME

I'M SO EXCITED BONNIE INVITED ME TO HANG OUT WITH HER FRIENDS FOR THANKSGIVING!

WON'T YOUR MOM BE MAD YOU'RE NOT SPENDING IT WITH HER?

PLEASE

SHE'LL NEVER NOTICE I'M NOT THERE

WELL ... I'LL BE SAD YOU WON'T BE AROUND FOR OUR TRADITIONAL POST-THANKSGIVING GRIPE FEST

HEY!

YOU WANNA COME ALONG?

YES ... WHY, YES I WOULD!

71

HI!

HEY, WELCOME!

HATTIE, YOU REMEMBER STUART

OH YEAH! DIDN'T I *BODY SLAM* YOU ONCE?

I'LL NEVER FORGET IT!

MY LOVELY WIFE AMY IS IN THE KITCHEN, HARD AT WORK

HATTIE, QUIT CHATTING AND START GETTING OUR GUESTS DRINKS!

YES, HONEY

OH! AND WHO'S THIS?

SORRY, THIS IS MY ROOMMATE CHERYL. I HOPE IT'S OKAY I BROUGHT HER ALONG

I DON'T LIKE TO BE TOUCHED

KNOCK KNOCK HAPPY THANKSGIVING!

AW, FRAN!

I DIDN'T KNOW YOU WERE COMING!

HAVING FUN?

STUART, COME MEET FRESH MEAT FRAN!

WOOP!

BEING SUMMONED, BRB!

≷SIGH≷

HE WILL BE MINE. OH YES . . . HE WILL BE MINE

CHERYL, I'D LIKE YOU TO MEET FRAN

HELLO!

FRAN *LOVES* BONNIE, SINCE BONNIE TOOK HER UNDER HER WING

IT'S TRUE!

YOU CAN'T MEET A SWEETER PERSON

HOW AWESOME IS IT THAT YOU GET TO HANG OUT WITH HER SO MUCH, LIVING WITH STUART AND ALL

HOW MANY TIMES HAVE YOU BEEN HIT IN THE HEAD?

JUST CURIOUS

YOU KNOW THAT ROOMMATE OF STUART'S HAS A CRUSH ON HIM

OH?

IT LOOKS LIKE THE WHOLE UNREQUITED THING

YOU MIGHT WANT TO WATCH OUT FOR HER

PLEASE

I ALREADY HAVE A PLAN IN PLACE TO MAKE CHERYL LOVE ME

BESIDES, IF THERE'S ONE THING DERBY HAS BEATEN INTO ME, IT'S THAT I CAN GET ALONG WITH *ANYONE*

AIN'T THAT THE TRUTH

POOR GIRL WON'T KNOW WHAT HIT HER

73

8 Coaches

Valentine Wishes

WE SHOULD BRAINSTORM HOW TO GET SKATERS TO STICK AROUND LONGER

WHAT DOES THAT MEAN?

HOW ABOUT FAIRER DISTRIBUTION OF LABOR?

MAYBE NOT MAKING THE FRESH MEAT DO *EVERY* JOB?

BUT THAT'S **TRADITION!**

JUST LOOK AT HOW MUCH FUN FRAN IS HAVING OVER THERE!

HOW IS THIS HELPING ME TO DERBY BETTER?

STUART!

WHAT'S UP MAN!

I HAVEN'T SEEN YOU IN A WHILE

SMACK

I WAS WORRIED YOU CAUGHT THE DERBY PLAGUE

OH, NO -- BONNIE'S IN RIDICULOUSLY GOOD HEALTH

SO I DON'T THINK SHE COULD EVER GET ME SICK

I MEANT WHERE YOU'RE SICK TO DEATH OF HOW DERBY IS OCCUPYING ALL OF YOUR WOMAN'S TIME

CAN WE TALK?

HEY, CAN YOU PASS THIS DOWN?

BONNIE'S TRYING TO GET ALL THE SKATERS TO FILL OUT THIS SURVEY

WHAT?

FRAN, WE'RE KIND OF BUSY RIGHT NOW

HERE?

OF COURSE, OF COURSE

≥FWEEET!≤

SO HOW WOULD YOU RATE THIS BOUTING EXPERIENCE ON A SCALE OF 1 TO 10?

FRAN!

ELEVEN IF WE WIN . . .

NOW ON TO . . .

THE **GROUP** SATISFACTION CHART!

THE HIGHEST LEVEL OF SATISFACTION GOES TO THE FRESH MEAT

THEY DON'T KNOW ANY BETTER

THEN THE TRAVEL TEAM . . .

THE HIGH SCHOOL SENIORS OF DERBY

THEN THE TEAM CAPTAINS . . .

WHO CAN GUESS WHICH GROUP OF SKATERS IS AT THE **LOWEST** SATISFACTION LEVEL?

GEE, MAYBE THE **INJURED** SKATERS, SINCE THAT'S THE ONLY GROUP LEFT?

CORRECT!

SO CLEARLY WE NEED TO ELIMINATE ALL INJURIES

IF DERBY IS TO SUCCEED.

SO LADIES, HOW SHOULD WE PROCEED?

WE NEED SOME WAY TO BRIDGE THE GAP BETWEEN HAPPY AND UNHAPPY SKATERS

CLAP!

DERBY BIG SISTERS!

THEY DO IT IN OTHER LEAGUES!

OH YEAH! PAIR UP SKATERS WITH DIFFERENT SKILLS

ALL TO WORK TOGETHER

AWESOME!

PROBLEM SOLVED!

HIGH FIVE!

OH GOD

PLEASE DON'T PAIR ME WITH AGRO AMELIA

THERE WOULD BE SO **MANY** INJURIES . . .

87

9 Herb in Charge

90

91

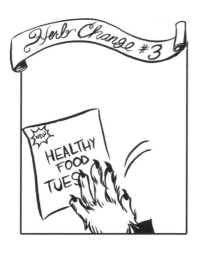

Herb Change #3

NEW

HEALTHY FOOD TUES

ONCE A WEEK, LET'S ALL GET TOGETHER AND SHARE SOME HEALTHY, HOMEMADE SNACKS

NO FAST FOOD ALLOWED!

SO WHO WANTS TO SHARE WHAT THEY'VE BROUGHT?

WE'LL DISCUSS HOW HEALTHY IT IS

I THOUGHT WE AGREED THAT LUNCH WAS A TABOO TOPIC

I BET YOU *MY* MYSTERY MEAT IS HEALTHIER THAN *YOUR* MYSTERY MEAT

≥GAG≤

LISTEN UP, MUSES –

WE JUST GOT INVITED TO BOUT WITH AN OUT OF STATE TEAM!

WOO!

CAP'N

SO YOU KNOW WHAT THAT MEANS

FUNDRAISING TIME!

≥GROAN≤

≥SIGH≤

WHO'S GOT IDEAS? GUEST BARTENDING? CARWASH? BAKE SALE?

BLEH

SORRY GUYS BUT IT WORKS!

WE COULD HAVE A CONTEST TO SEE WHO COULD KNOCK DOWN ARTIE CHOKE-HOLD!

YEAH!

A.K.A. NO ONE.

NOW REMEMBER, LADIETH -- 25% OF ALL THE DRINKS YOU SELL GOES TO **YOUR TEAM!**

THO LETH GET THOTH ORDERTH IN AND OUT ATH QUICK AS POTHIBLE!

AYE AYE, MOLLY

TEAM BARTENDING, WOO!

AND ABTHOLUTELY NO DRINKING OF ANY KIND WHILE ON THKATETH!

VWOOP!

CRASH

ANY KIND?

CATHE IN POINT

I'M NOT DRUNK! IT'S WET BACK HERE!

UGH, THIS SUCKS

WHAT?!

BARTENDING IS SO MUCH FUN!

ARE YOU KIDDING? BEING AN ALCOHOL WAITRESS IS FUN?

NO DRINKING WHEN YOU'RE ON THKATETH, LADIETH!

‹SIGH› WE KNOW, MOLLY

WHAT'S **NOT** TO LOVE ABOUT COMING UP WITH FUN COCKTAILS?

YOU KNOW YOU HAVE TO MAKE WHAT PEOPLE ORDER, DON'T YOU?

IF I MAKE THEM GOOD ENOUGH, THEY WON'T KNOW THE DIFFERENCE

95

ROUND TWO!

I'M SO GLAD YOU LIKE MY SIGNATURE DRINK! MIMI TOLD ME I WAS NUTS FOR TRYING TO COMBINE THAT MANY ALCOHOLS TOGETHER

WELL I'M ALREADY TIPSY, SO IT'S A SUCCESS!

≷WINCE≷

DUDE

AS BONNIE'S BEST FRIEND, I ADMIRE YOUR SACRIFICE

BUT YOU'RE AN IDIOT

≷COUGH≷

AND THATSH A WRAP! GREAT JOB, MUTHETH*! YOU MADE ENOUGH MONEY TO TRAVEL TO THE BOUT!

*MUSES

WOOOO!

≷GROAN≷

POOR STUART! I WONDER WHAT HAPPENED? FOOD POISONING?

SOMETHING LIKE THAT

UHHH . . . BONNIE?

YES STUART?

I HAVE RAINBOWS RISING UP IN MY THROAT

97

KNOCK KNOCK

STUART?

MMF

BONNIE LEFT THIS NO --

MMRFLE

HMM?

CRUMPLE

UH ... I SAID HOW ARE YOU FEELING?

WANT SOME COFFEE?

≥GROAN≤

UGH

'MORNING!

SO CHERYL, I DIDN'T-- I WASN'T TOO GROSS LAST NIGHT, WAS I?

LIKE WITH ALL THE VOMITING?

OH THANK GOD

OH NO, NO WORRIES

I CAN'T SEE BONNIE EVER KISSING ME AGAIN AFTER WATCHING ME PUKE MY GUTS OUT

OH, SHE SAW

WHAT?!

YEAH, SHE WAS HERE

NOOO ...

IN FACT, I THINK AT ONE POINT YOU EVEN PUKED ON HER

≥WHINE≤

10 Out-of-State Bout

ARE WE RIVALS BECAUSE THEY'RE VEGANS AND WE'RE NOT?

NOPE

BECAUSE OUR CAPTAIN USED TO DATE THEIR CAPTAIN?

NOPE

IS IT BECAUSE THEIR TEAM COLORS ARE COMPLIMENTARY TO OURS?

NOPE

WELCOME, MUSES!

YOU GUYS READY TO GET YOUR PATOOTIES KICKED?

IS IT BECAUSE OF HER SWEET TUTU?

THESE NEXT FEW STRIPS FEATURE **MIMI MASSACRE**, OF "GIRLS WITH SLINGSHOTS" FAME! DANIELLE CORSETTO
(AKA THE CREATOR OF GWS) GRACIOUSLY LET ME BORROW HER FOR A BIT SO SHE COULD PLAY WITH MY DERBY PEEPS.

HI EVERYONE! I'M MIMI MASSACRE

IS IT BECAUSE SHE'S ALSO A **MIMI?**

SSH!

MAKE YOURSELVES AT HOME!

WE'VE GOT A LOCKER FOR YOUR GEAR ..

WATER BOTTLES AND CANDY FOR REFRESHMENTS

AND AFTER THE BOUT, WE CAN ALL GO OUT FOR **CUPCAKES AND ALCOHOL!**

THIS IS A MAGICAL, MAGICAL PLACE

RIVALS, BONNIE!

LOYALTY ... BEING TESTED ..

OH, AND IF YOU GUYS ARE UP FOR IT, WE ALSO HAVE A REGULAR BOARD GAME NIGHT --

AAHHH

SO FRAN, WHAT'S YOUR POISON? GUYS OR GALS?

UM, WELL

GIRLS - I GUESS

GALS IT IS! LET'S SEE... WHAT ABOUT HER?

SHE'S PETITE, CUTE GLASSES

OOH, SORRY, THAT'S LEMON CELLO - SHE'S STRAIGHT

WHAT'S UM -- WHAT'S HER STORY?

OOH, GOOD CALL, FRAN

THAT'S VIOLET PUNCH! RECENTLY SINGLE, PROBABLY NOT LOOKING FOR ANYTHING SERIOUS. GOOD FLING POTENTIAL!

WHAT ABOUT HER? SHE'S SKINNY, SMALL LIKE YOU FRAN

BONNIE, ARE YOU PICKING OUT WOMEN FOR FRAN BASED ON IF THEY'RE THE SAME CLOTHES SIZE?

WHY, IS THAT WEIRD?

MATCHMAKING SUCCESS!

BOO YEAH!

SO... MIMI

HMM?

TELL ME --

WHAT'S THE SECRET?

WHAT SECRET?

WHY OUR TEAMS ARE RIVALS!

OH!

BEATS ME

WHAT! YOU DON'T KNOW EITHER??

I ALWAYS ASSUMED IT WAS BECAUSE YOU GUYS STOLE OUR MASCOT DESIGN

LOOKS LIKE THEY'RE GETTING ON WELL

SO CUTE! BUT - WAIT...

WHAT'S AGRO AMELIA DO --

OH NO! SHE'S GOT **TWO** DRINKS! SHE WAS MOVING IN BEFORE FRAN GOT THERE!

ABORT!

ABORT!

CRAP, WHAT DO WE DO? AMELIA ALREADY BEATS UP ON FRAN **SO MUCH**

HMM

HAVE YOU EVER HEARD OF THE **TAP-TAP-SLAM**?

NO, BUT IT SOUNDS AMAZING

JUST FOLLOW MY LEAD - I'LL DO THE TAP-TAP, YOU COME IN FOR THE SLAM

HEYYY

HUH?

tap tap

WHATCHA - OH! SORRY, I THOUGHT YOU --

SLAM

OH GOD AMELIA I'M SORRY!

COME ON, LET'S GO GET YOU CLEANED UP!

OH, THIS HAS BEEN SO MUCH FUN, I'M BUMMED TO LEAVE!

COME BACK ANYTIME FOR AN ASS WHOOPIN'!

SOO FRANNNN

DID YOU GET VIOLET'S DIGITS?

NO, HER HANDS WERE TOO BRUISED FOR ME TO HOLD

OH -≥SNORT≤ NO, DIGITS AS IN HER *PHONE NUMBER*

YOU KNOW, THAT'S FROM CLUELESS

WHAT'S THAT?

OH MY GOD. THE MOVIE *CLUELESS.* IT WAS RELEASED IN LIKE '95

OH SORRY, THEN I WAS FIVE WHEN IT CAME OUT ≥GASP≤

WE'RE SOOOO OLDDD...

I WAS HOPING TO HEAR SOMETHING FROM HER BY NOW

IT'S BEEN ALMOST A WEEK...

DUDE.

SORRY, WHAT?

COULD YOU *NOT* CHECK YOUR PHONE TO SEE IF YOUR GIRLFRIEND TEXTED YOU LIKE, EVERY FIVE SECONDS?

OH, I'M SORRY GUYS, I --≥≤

RUDE

THE WORST

HEY CHERYL. OH --

ARE YOU EXPECTING SOMEONE? I CAN LEAVE --

NO!

NOPE, NOT EXPECTING ANYONE ... DO YOU WANT SOME FOOD?

... SURE

HOW WAS YOUR DAY? CAN I MAKE YOU A COCKTAIL?

UH

SO HAVE YOU HEARD FROM BONNIE LATELY?

NO ...

I'M STARTING TO GET A LITTLE WORRIED

CHERYL, DO YOU REMEMBER THE NIGHT WHEN I WAS SICK?

I WAS SO OUT OF IT -- ARE YOU SURE BONNIE DIDN'T SAY ANYTHING ABOUT NOT CALLING FOR A WHILE?

NOPE.

DAMN

KNOCK KNOCK

HI STUART! I'M BACK!

BONNIE?

I MEAN YES! YES SHE DID LEAVE A NOTE!

11 Bonnie V. Summer

GREAT JOB OUT THERE, HERB! YOU REALLY GRABBED THE BULL BY THE HORNS!

THANK YOU, BONNIE

IT GOES FOR YOU AS WELL

NO PROBLEM! I JUST WANTED TO CHAT WITH YOU ABOUT THE FALL PICNIC

YOU KNOW, *MY* ANNUAL TRADITION!

NOT THIS YEAR

WHAT??

I'M GOING TO GIVE IT TO SHERRY AND BARB TO PLAN

B-BUT THEY'RE SUMMER WORSHIPPERS - THEY DON'T EVEN *LIKE* FALL!

SORRY BONNIE, GOTTA GIVE OTHER EMPLOYEES THE CHANCE TO --

SHERRY STILL HAS A SUNBURN!

CAN YOU BELIEVE IT'S SIXTY-FIVE FREAKING DEGREES OUT?

I KNOW, IT'S **FREEZING.** I HAD TO PUT ON A *SWEATER!* THIS SUCKS!

SCREECH

MURDER

SABOTAGE? IS THE *WEREWOLF* UM -- *HERB* .. DOING IT AGAIN?

NO, WORSE

SHERRY AND BARBARA

THEY *HATE* SWEATER WEATHER AND LEAVES IN THEIR HAIR AND CORN MAZES AND PUMPKINS!

THEY SHOULD BE DISQUALIFIED!

WELL, TO BE FAIR - NO ONE LIKES FALL THE WAY THAT *YOU* LIKE FALL

ACTUALLY, IN LIGHT OF RECENT EVENTS, I THINK NO ONE LIKES FALL THE WAY THAT *I* LIKE FALL . . .

STUART, GET YOUR HEAD IN THE GAME!

SO WHAT'LL IT BE?

WELL FIRST I NEED SOME INTEL ON WHAT THEY'RE PLANNING

UNFORTUNATELY, HERB HAS DECLARED SHERRY AND BARB'S CUBE A *BONNIE-FREE ZONE*

I HAVE A MAN ON THE INSIDE, BUT SO FAR HIS REPORTS HAVE LACKED ANY REAL *DETAIL*

tap tap

BONNIE - REMEMBER, YOU PROMISED ME A DATE WITH A *HOT* ROLLER GIRL FOR THIS. BARB'S FILING HER NAILS AND SHERRY IS BRUSHING HER HAIR

A *HOT* ONE!

tap tap tap

CREAK

H - HELLO?

ARE YOU THE LIAISON?

YEAH, BONNIE SENT

SSH! NO NAMES!

WORD ON THE STREET IS THAT THE PICNIC WILL TAKE PLACE AT *PANAMA BEACH BAR*...

AT DUSK!

WAIT --

THE FALL PICNIC IS BEING HELD ... AT A **SPORTS BAR**?

OHH BONNIE IS NOT GONNA LIKE THIS ONE BIT.

FIDGET FIDGET

THIS CONVERSATION NEVER HAPPENED.

BUT -- HEY, HER ROLLERGIRL FRIENDS ARE *HOT*, RIGHT?

PANAMA BEACH BAR

WHERE IT'S SUMMER YEAR ROUND!

WELCOME!

CUBE FARM COMPANY PICNIC 5pm-close

YOU SURE YOU WANNA DO THIS?

MORE THAN ANYTHING

YOU KNOW, WE COULD HAVE A FEW DRINKS, HANG OUT ..

GO GET SOME PUMPKIN PIE ...

USE IT FOR *GOOD*, STUART!

THIS IS THE BEST COMPANY PICNIC EVER!

OONTZ

WOOO!

OONTZ OONTZ

OONTZ OONTZ

I GOTTA PEE!

ME TOO!

SLAM

HELLO, LADIES.

WHERE ARE WE?

DID YOU *PAINT* THIS WHOLE BATHROOM?!

YES, TO TEACH YOU A LESSON!

YOU'RE IN HERE BECAUSE YOU NEED TO LEARN ABOUT FALL ... ABOUT OCTOBER!

ABOUT *HALLOWEEN!*

AND WHAT BETTER PLACE TO TEACH YOU THAN THE BATHROOM FROM THE SHINING?

IT TOOK *FIVE COATS* OF RED PAINT, WHO KNEW?

WE'RE IN HERE BECAUSE WE NEED TO **PEE**

WHAT'S THE SHINING?

YOU'RE IN HERE TO LEARN SOME RESPECT!

slurp

HOW COME THERE'S A HUGE LINE OUTSIDE THE GIRL'S BATHROOM?

UM... BECAUSE THEY'RE *GIRLS*?

HOW DO *YOU* THINK IT'S GOING IN THERE?

GREAT

SHE'S PROBABLY CONVERTED THEM ALREADY

BONNIE HAS SOME OF THE CRAZIEST IDEAS, BUT I NEVER DOUBT SHE'LL SUCCEED

SHE'S *BRILLIANTLY* NUTS

IT'S GOOD TO BE ME

WE PISH!

JESUS, DUDE, *WHIPPED* MUCH?

SLAM

YOU'RE CRAZY! STAY AWAY FROM US,

YEAH, BACK OFF!

BUT YOU GUYS HAVEN'T EVEN PLAYED THE GAMES!

WE'RE NOT PLAYING ANY STUPID GAMES, BONNIE! THE LAST THING WE'D EVER WANT IS TO BE LIKE *YOU*!

YEAH!

AND THAT SHELLEY DUVALL MOVIE CAN SUCK IT!

⟨GASP⟩ YOU REMEMBER THAT SHELLEY DUVALL PLAYS WENDY IN THE SHINING!

NO, WE --

SUCCESS HUGS!

ACK!

≥AHEM≤!

OH!

HI CARL

I JUST WANTED TO SEE WHEN YOU WERE GOING TO UPHOLD YOUR END OF THE BARGAIN . . . AND ARRANGE THAT *DATE* WITH A ROLLERGIRL FOR ME

AND I THINK IT GOES WITHOUT SAYING THAT I DESERVE A **SLUTTY** ONE FOR THE EFFORT I GAVE!

A DEAL'S A *DEAL*!

DON'T YOU WORRY, CARL

A ROLLERGIRL *ALWAYS* PAYS HER DEBTS

DOUCHEY GUY AT MY WORK WANTS TO DATE A "SLUTTY ROLLERGIRL" - WHO WANTS TO DELIVER THE BEATING?

ME!

OOH, ME!

≥SIGH≤

WHAT'S UP?

OH, Y'KNOW - SEASON'S WINDING DOWN - IT'S JUST A LITTLE SAD, IS ALL

WHAT? BUT THIS IS WHEN WE GET TO PUT ON OUR **WINTER WEIGHT** - TUCK IN AND GET *COZY* BEFORE WE HAVE TO SWEAT IT OFF NEXT SEASON!

WHAT'S TO BE *SAD* ABOUT?

I GUESS I JUST MISS GETTING TO *HIT* PEOPLE

CLEARLY YOU HAVE A DIFFERENT THANKSGIVING EXPERIENCE THAN I DO

Derby Wife DATE NIGHT

SO WHAT'S NEW?

MMM... NOT MUCH

OH... EXCEPT I GOT A CALL BACK FOR THAT NATURAL RESOURCES SPECIALIST JOB

WHAT!

MIMI, THAT'S HUGE!

IT IS!

BUT... WON'T YOU HAVE TO TRAVEL A LOT?

YEAH

WON'T IT BE HARDER MAKING PRACTICES?

YEAH

AND COMMITTEE REQUIREMENTS?

FOR SURE

YOU'RE NOT...

YOU'RE NOT GONNA QUIT DERBY...

OH HELL NO!

YOU KNOW, IT'S LIKE EVERYTHING ELSE... DERBY'S A PART OF MY LIFE

DAMN SKIPPY

SO... FREE TIME?

DOWN TO ZILCH

AND I HAVEN'T HAD A **DATE** IN I DON'T KNOW HOW LONG

AHEM!

AND JUST WHAT IS **THIS** WE'RE ON?

OH HUSH

YOU SEE THAT CANDLE? THAT WINE? I BELIEVE **THIS** IS A DATE.

A DERBY DATE

WITH MY SOON-TO-BE DERBY **EX**-WIFE

I'M DERBY CHOPPED LIVER?

YOU ARE

THINGS CHANGE SO QUICKLY IN DERBY. PEOPLE ARE ALWAYS COMING AND GOING

RETIRING, HAVING A BABY, MOVING TO A NEW CITY

GETTING INJURED

I FINALLY MEET A GROUP OF COOL, INTERESTING WOMEN AND THEY NEVER... STAY STILL, Y'KNOW?

≥SNORT≤

WELL, THEY WOULDN'T, IN DERBY!

WELL I'M STILL HERE

AND I'M THANKFUL

FOR NOW, ANYWAY

BITE YOUR TONGUE!

UNTIL SOMETHING BETTER COMES ALONG

AW, YOU'RE RUINING THE MOMENT!

CLICK

MUSES

12 Drafting Fran

DONUT TOWN

I'M SERIOUSLY BEGINNING TO WONDER ABOUT YOU AND YOUR OBSESSION WITH ROUND TABLES

WHAT'S GOOD ENOUGH FOR KING ARTHUR, AM I RIGHT?

≷SIGH≷

HEY GUYS! OVER HERE!

HEY MUSES!

YOU GUYS READY TO CHAT ABOUT NEXT SEA--

AAH!

YOU ALRIGHT THERE, CHIEF?

I CAN'T CONTAIN MY EXCITEMENT FOR NEW TEAMMATES

RIGHT NOW WE HAVE THREE VACANT SPOTS TO FILL AT THE DRAFT

WE'RE IN NEED OF TWO SOLID BLOCKERS AND SOMEONE NIMBLE ENOUGH TO GET THROUGH THAT WALL THE SIRENS ALWAYS PUT UP FOR US

A.K.A. SCYLLA AND CHARYBDIS

THE TWO TOWERS

NERD ALERT!

FOR WHICH?

LORD OF THE RINGS IS A WAY NERDIER REFERENCE

NO ONE'S A WINNER HERE

I THINK YOU'RE MISSING THE POINT OF BEING ON A TEAM

THE BEAUTY OF IT IS, THEY *CHOOSE* YOU, WHICH MEANS THEY WANT YOU!

AND AS YOUR TEAMMATES, IT'S IN *THEIR* BEST INTEREST TO BUILD UP YOUR SKILLS AND PROTECT YOU!

I GUESS

AND, IF YOU *DO* GET TEAMED WITH AGRO AMELIA, THEN YOU KNOW IN SCRIMMAGE AND BOUTS SHE WON'T TOUCH YOU!

HOW AWESOME IS THAT?

WAIT . . . SO NOW I SHOULD *WANT* TO BE ON AMELIA'S TEAM?

OH --

I WOULDN'T SAY *THAT*

BEING IN THE FRESH MEAT POOL HAS JUST BEEN SO MUCH FUN

I GET TO PLAY WITH *ALL* OF YOU AND NEVER HAVE TO PICK SIDES

BUT WHEN I'M TEAMED --

WILL I STILL GET TO HANG OUT WITH YOU?

HA HA HA, OF *COURSE*, SILLY!

UNLESS, OF COURSE, YOU GET ON THE *SIRENS*

THEY'RE OUR MORTAL ENEMIES

YOU UNDERSTAND

HOORAY! CONGRATS, FRAN! YOU MADE IT THROUGH THE TEST!

CONGRATS!

HI STUART!

LET'S GET YOU A CELEBRATION DRINK!

BUT I DON'T EVEN KNOW IF I'M ON A **TEAM** YET

YOU DID **YOUR** PART, YOU TOOK THE TEST! NOW YOU GET TO HAVE FUN!

SEE? LOOK AT ALL THE OTHER DRAFTEES HERE, ENJOYING THEMSELVES!

IS FRAN HAVING A GOOD TIME? SHE'S CHECKING HER PHONE MORE THAN **I** DO WHEN I'M UNCOMFORTABLE IN PUBLIC

YEAH, IT'S HARD FOR THE POOR FRESHIES

THE COACHES ARE DELIBERATING NOW ABOUT WHO GETS DRAFTED AND WHO DOESN'T

RIGHT **NOW**? SHEESH, NO WONDER

THEY COULD BE TOLD AT ANY MOMENT

DO YOU THINK IF WE GOT FRAN WASTED AND DANCING THAT WOULD TAKE HER MIND OFF IT?

WELLL . .

BARTENDER!

WE'LL HAVE A **BONNIE SPECIAL** OVER HERE PLEASE!

UH . . . THAT'S NOT WHAT I **THINK** IT IS, IS IT?

YUP, THE RAINBOW SURPRISE, YOUR FAVORITE!

COMING RIGHT UP!

I NEED TO GET TO FRAN

WHATSA MATTER? ARE YOU AS EXCITED AS I AM TO GO TO HERB'S HOUSE??

EEEEE...

WELL, UM -

I MEAN, I'D *LIKE* TO BE EXCITED

I GUESS IT'S JUST ... I'M NOT **FAMILIAR** WITH WERE-WOLVES LIKE YOU ARE

WHAT DO THEY ... DO FOR ... ≶AHEM≶

F-FUN?

HM, I DUNNO -- I'VE ONLY EVER MET HERB

AND I KNOW HE'S VERY TIDY, HAS HIS TAILOR ON SPEED DIAL ...

WILL HE EAT US??

STUART, I WANT TO ASK YOU AND BONNIE ON A DOUBLE DATE WITH STEVE AND I

OH REALLLY!

STEVE, THE GUY WHO HAS A CRUSH ON YOU!

YES, HE'S CLEARLY OBSESSED WITH ME, SO I WANT TO SEE WHAT HE HAS TO OFFER

WHEN ARE YOU TWO AVAILABLE?

I'M NOT SURE, BONNIE'S USUALLY SUPER BUSY-

≶GASP≶ YOU GUYS COULD COME *WITH* US TO HERB'S HOUSE!

BONNIE'S FRIENDS WITH THIS GUY WHO **TERRIFIES** ME! BUT IF YOU AND STEVE COME, IT'LL TAKE THE PRESSURE OFF!

STUART NEEDING ME IS THE CHINK IN BONNIE'S ARMOR

OF COURSE I'LL HELP! I MEAN, WE'LL HELP

THANKS CHERYL. I OWE YOU **BIG**!

STEVE, I'D LIKE TO ASK YOU TO GO ON A DATE WITH ME

BUT BEFORE YOU GET *TOO* EXCITED, HERE ARE SOME THINGS YOU SHOULD KNOW:

A) IT'S ALSO WITH FOUR OTHER PEOPLE

B) ONE OF THOSE PEOPLE I HAVE A CRUSH ON

NO THANKS, CHERYL - IT SOUNDS LIKE A LOT OF DRAMA AND I'M NOT INTERESTED IN BEING USED LIKE THAT

BUT YOU DIDN'T LET ME FINISH!

C) ONE OF THOSE PEOPLE MIGHT HAPPEN TO BE A WEREWOLF!

I'M LISTENING

SO HERB'S OKAY WITH CHERYL AND STEVE COMING TOO?

YUP, LUCKY FOR *YOU*!

I'M SORRY, BONNIE. I DIDN'T MEAN TO MAKE THINGS AWKWARD, I JUST --

BUT HE DID SAY HE'S PUTTING YOU ON HIS NAUGHTY LIST ... WHATEVER *THAT* MEANS

PUNCH

YOU'RE SO EASY! DON T WORRY, HERB'S GONNA *LOVE* YOU!

YES ...

LOVE ME ... ON A PLATE ..

WELCOME!

≥GASP≤! BUSINESS CASUAL HERB!

YOU'RE WEARING A SWEATER VEST!

AND YOU'RE NOT WEARING SKATES! WE'RE BOTH OUT OF OUR ELEMENT, HAHA!

STUART, IS IT? PLEASURE TO MEET YOU

AAH!

I'M SORRY, IT'S JUST SUCH AN HONOR TO MEET A WEREWOLF ... IN *REAL LIFE*!

HONEY, THIS DINNER PARTY IS A *SCREAM* ALREADY!

BONNIE, STUART-- THIS IS STEVE

HI STEVE!

GREAT TO MEET YOU!

WHY THE BINOCULARS, IF YOU DON'T MIND ME ASKING?

OH, WHEN CHERYL SAID WE MIGHT SEE A WEREWOLF TONIGHT, I DIDN'T KNOW IF SHE MEANT LITERALLY OR FIGURATIVELY

I'M A MEMBER OF THE BIGFOOT SOCIETY! WE'RE ALL ABOUT FINDING PROOF THAT BIGFOOT EXISTS AND LETTING THE WORLD KNOW!

THAT'S RIGHT -- THIS GUY'S MY DATE. GO AHEAD AND BE JEALOUS.

DOESN'T EVERY-ONE ALREADY KNOW BIGFOOT EXISTS?

GENTLEMEN! YOU WILL BE MY CO-CONSPIRATORS!

≷GULP≷

≷GASP≷ WEREWOLF SECRETS!

ACCORDING TO MY NEW BEST FRIEND - THIS DINNER PARTY MANUAL - YOU NEED **THREE THINGS** FOR A SUCCESSFUL PARTY

AND NUMBER ONE IS ATMOSPHERE!

WHOOPS, I FORGOT THE *CANDLES!*

PARDON ME!

QUICK, STEVE -- GET THE MANUAL!

DOES IT SAY "TO SERVE MAN" ON IT??

"HANDBOOK FOR THE RECENTLY DINING"

SO WHAT ARE THE OTHER TWO NECESSITIES FOR A PARTY, HERB? FOOD AND DRINK?

OH MY DEAR BOY, NO!

THE SECOND IS **PATIENCE** - FOR FOOD TO COOK, WINE TO DECANT, GUESTS TO CONVERSE!

AND THE LAST ONE?

THE LAST ONE, OF COURSE, IS *DRAMA!*

I DON'T KNOW ABOUT THAT WITH US - WE'RE A PRETTY *LOW-KEY* GROUP

THAT'S NOT WHAT I HEAR!

WORD ON THE STREET IS **CHERYL** IS IN LOVE WITH *STUART,* WHO IS IN LOVE WITH **BONNIE**

STUPENDOUS!

139

I SHOULD -- I NEED TO TALK TO CHERYL

OKAY, NO PROBLEM

BYE, HERB! THANK YOU!

DON'T FORGET YOUR GIFT BAGS!

HEY, GUYS -

SORRY, BUT . . . CAN I GET A RIDE? CHERYL BROUGHT ME . . .

OF COURSE!

AWKWARD

SORRY, I HAVE TO GO

I'LL GIVE YOU A CALL LATER

AWKWARDER

SO YOUR DATE WENT PRETTY WELL!

I MEAN, ASIDE FROM WHEN YOUR DATE CONFESSED HER LOVE FOR MY DATE

≷GASP≶
OPERATION PETTICOAT! . . . IMPLODED!

OHHH NO, I'M NOT GIVING UP -- SOONER OR LATER, CHERYL WILL *LOVE ME!*

WELL THAT'S EASY - JUST DRESS LIKE STUART!

STUART WAS *SO* SHOCKED. . . I MEAN, HIS BFF BEING SECRETLY IN LOVE WITH HIM THIS *WHOLE TIME*

I DUNNO, DO YOU THINK--

NOPE! HE'S HAD A TASTE OF THE *BONNIE* . . . YOU DON'T RECOVER FROM THAT SHIT.

So, whatcha been thinkin' about?

Oh, I dunno...

I've just put so much time and energy into derby, y'know

So when I didn't get on a **team**, I kind of felt like ... what's the point?

Just because you're not on a team, doesn't mean you're not in derby!

Or not still a kick-ass roller girl!

You think I got onto a team - into a *league* - on the first try?

Well.. yeah

Ha ha -- you have **no idea** how many years this face has been learning to skate.

BONNIE'S PAST... *Oooo...*

DERBY IS MY *LIFE*

I can't be stopped!

Here we go...

eeek eeek

OMG I've never gone this fast

I am doing **amazing!**

145

WHEN I WAS A NEWBIE SKATER, EVERY LITTLE STEP WAS A *HUGE* ACHIEVEMENT!

HEY! MY LEGS STOPPED LOCKING UP ON ME AFTER SKATING FOR TEN MINUTES!

HEY! I SKATED FROM RINK TO CARPET WITHOUT FALLING ON MY FACE!

LOOKIN' GOOD, FRESHIE!

KEEP IT UP!

HEY! I STOPPED COMPARING MYSELF TO BETTER SKATERS!

DERBY ACHIEVEMENT UNLOCKED

SO WHAT YOU'RE SAYING IS THAT I SHOULDN'T GIVE UP

AARGH OF *COURSE* YOU SHOULDN'T!

WHAT DO I ALWAYS SAY?

NEVER GIVE UP?

NOPE

SHUTUP AND SKATE?

UH-UH

WHEN LIFE GIVES YOU LEMONS . . .

UMM . . .

OH!

WHY BE LAME WHEN YOU CAN BE IN DERBY?

DING DING DING!

ALRIGHT

JUST GOTTA KEEP REMINDING MYSELF THAT IT'S NOT ALL *THAT* EMBARRASSING I DIDN T GET ON A TEAM... I MEAN, IT'S BEST SOMETHING LIKE THIS HAPPENS WHEN NO ONE REALLY NOTICES ME ANYWAY...

HI FRAN!

THE HELL'VE YOU BEEN?

OKAY, SO MAYBE I *DO* KIND OF BELONG HERE

QUIT POKIN' AROUND AND GET YER SKATES ON!

WHAT'RE YOU ALL PUFFED UP ABOUT?

OH, NOTHING

JUST SAVING THE WORLD, ONE SKATER AT A TIME

LOOK! FRAN'S BACK!

I SEE

WHO'S GOT TWO THUMBS AND IS UNDEFEATED IN PULLING SKATERS BACK FROM THE BRINK?

THE ONE TRYING UNSUCCESSFULLY TO MOONWALK IN SKATES?

13 Relocating Stuart

153

HERE'S TO 'S, GEORGE --

NEW ROOMIES!

HEH

SO NOW THAT **YOU AND GEORGE** ARE LIVING TOGETHER, WHAT ARE ALBERT AND I SUPPOSED TO DO?

WHAT DO YOU MEAN?

WE HAVE TO MAKE SURE TO PRESERVE THE *GROUP* DYNAMIC!

ALL OF US **EQUAL** FRIENDS!

IT CAN'T SWAY TOO HEAVILY TO **EITHER** PAIR!

WELL UNTIL GEORGE AND I SIGN PAPERS ON THE NEW PLACE, I'LL BE STAYING WITH ALBERT . . .

BOOM

AW COME ON!

HOLY CRAP, MAN! LONG TIME, NO SEE

HI TED!

I HAVEN'T SEEN BONNIE IN A LITTLE WHILE . . . I FIGURED THIS WAS THE PLACE SHE'D **HAVE** TO BE!

OH? WHAT'S BEEN GOING ON?

YEAH. I'VE BEEN DEALING WITH A LOT OF STUFF LATELY WITH MY BEST FRIEND, MOVING, **FINDING** A NEW PLACE TO LIVE . . .

I WANTED TO *SPARE* BONNIE ALL THAT CRAP

--OH! THERE SHE IS

STUART, DERBY IS LIKE THE OCEAN . . .

WHO'S THAT GUY SHE'S TALKING TO?

TURN YOUR BACK ON IT, AND YOU MIGHT GET DRAGGED OUT TO SEA

SHE'S NOT . . .

BONNIE'S NOT . . . *DATING* SOMEONE ELSE NOW, IS SHE?

OH GOD, SHE'S DATING SOMEONE ELSE

NAW, MAN - CHILL OUT

I DON'T THINK SO ANYWAY - HAS IT REALLY BEEN *THAT* LONG SINCE YOU'VE SEEN HER?

THE LAST TIME I SAW BONNIE, MY BEST FRIEND TOLD ME *SHE* LOVED ME

. . . AND I WENT HOME WITH MY *FRIEND* INSTEAD

TO *FIX* THINGS!

STOP

NOT TO, LIKE, HAVE SEX WITH MY FRIEND!

YOU'RE BLOWIN' THROUGH ALL SORT OF SIGNS ON THIS JOURNEY, MAN

I SAW YOUR NERDY LITTLE BOY TOY

WHO, STUART?

STUART WAS HERE? AWW . . .

YEAH, I SAW HIM OVER TALKING TO THE WIDOWS BEFORE

NOW . . . I DUNNO

RATS

WE'VE BEEN MISSING EACH OTHER FOR A WHILE

DID I TELL YOU HIS BFF CHERYL MADE HER *MOVE* ON HIM?

TSK, WHAT'D I TELL YOU

TICKING TIMEBOMB

I CAN STILL TOTALLY WIN HER OVER, Y KNOW

SURE YOU CAN, HON

PAT PAT

SHE *WILL* COME TO LOVE ME, YOU JUST WAI'

OH YEAH --

CUTE, EH?

THE STRAIGHT GIRLS ON THE LEAGUE HAVE GOT YOUR **NUMBER**

DO THEY NOW?

AND WHAT ABOUT YOU?

ARE YOU ONE OF THE **STRAIGHT GIRLS?**

IT'S WEIRD WHEN SOMEONE ASKS YOUR SEXUAL ORIENTATION WHEN YOU'VE ONLY JUST MET . . .

OH GOD

I DIDN'T MEAN IT LIKE THAT! HA HA

I JUST MEANT -- YOU WANT TO GO OUT SOMETIME?

HA!

YOU'RE CONFIDENT, TOO!

OH MAN - THEY ARE GOING TO **DESTROY** YOU (I MEAN, IN A SEXY WAY)

BUT ACTUALLY, I'M DATING SOMEONE

AH!

WHAT A SHAME

WELL, GOOD LUCK! IT'S THE **BEST** LEAGUE, SO I'M SURE YOU'LL ENJOY IT HERE

I DEFINITELY WILL

CREAK

BZZT BZZT

OH THANK GOD — SHE STILL LIKES ME

10:23

BONNIE:
STUART!!!!

>slide to unlock

It SUCKS I missed you at the bout! I'm on my way over!!

OHHH SHIT

KNOCK KNOCK

YOO HOO!

CREAK

BZZZ BZZZ BZZZ

HI CHERYL!

HOW ARE YOU?

ARE YOU SERIOUS?

GREAT, UM

HOME?

HERE?

IS STUART HOME YET?

I MEAN, I KNOW IT'S BEEN A WHILE, BUT HE STILL LIVES HERE, RIGHT?

WAS *TRYING* TO FIND SOME WAY TO BREAK YOU UP!

I'M *ALWAYS* LOOKING TO BREAK YOU TWO UP!

COME ON, BONNIE

LET'S GET OUT OF HERE

'BYE CHERYL

I'M IN *LOVE* WITH MY BEST FRIEND, SO OF *COURSE* I HATE HIS GIRLFRIEND!

SLAM!

HOW HARD IS THAT TO UNDERSTAND??

BONNIE, I'M SORRY WE HAVEN'T . . .

I MISSED YOU SO MUCH

DITTO

WANNA SHOW ME WHERE YOU LIVE FOR REAL NOW?

WE NEED IDEAS

WE NEED IDEAS FOR HOW TO STAY AWAY FROM *BONNIE*

THIS IS SO DUMB -- WHY DOESN'T HERB JUST HAVE BONNIE DO THE FALL PICNIC EVERY YEAR?

DUDE, HE'S A WEREWOLF -- CLEARLY HE'S INTO HUMAN TORTURE

SIGH

I GUESS . . .

I MEAN -- IT WAS PRETTY COOL SEEING BONNIE USE THE SHINING LAST YEAR ON SHERRY AND BARBARA

I REALLY THOUGHT SHE WAS GOING TO MAKE THE WALLS OF THAT SPORTS BAR *BLEED*

CARL - *THIS* YEAR, NOW *WE'RE* THE SHELLY DUVALLS

HE-ERRRB

READ THE SIGN, BONNIE

HRMPH

BUT . . .

NO POUTING ON SKATES

AH-AH! AND THE *OTHER* SIGN

HERB! THAT'S JUST GROSS

NO BUTTS ON SKATES

AND, APPARENTLY NECESSARY

HIIII GUYS

UH OH

DON'T LOOK DIRECTLY AT HER

DON'T WORRY, I'M NOT HERE TO INTERFERE! I JUST WANTED TO SEE IF YOU GUYS NEEDED ANY HELP

I KNOW WHERE TO GET THE BEST-LOOKING GOURDS!

WE'RE NOT USING GOURDS

OOOH, WHAT ARE YOU GUYS PLANNING?

DO YOU KNOW WHERE TO GET BARRELS OF MILK?

CARTONS OF TENNIS BALLS?

POUNDS OF MUSTARD?

THAT'LL THROW HER OFF THE SCENT FOR A WHILE

CUBE FARMS ANNUAL PICNIC

GRAB A WEAPON

GRAB A CLOAK

SO? HOW BAD IS IT?

IT'S NOT... IT LOOKS *FINE*, BONNIE!

REALLY? IS IT FALL APPROPRIATE?

THERE ARE HAY BALES

AND IT LOOKS LIKE A MAZE

BUT WE ALREADY DID A CORN MAZE ... AND WEAPONS? WE ALREADY *DID* THE HUNGER GAMES, TOO!

LOOK! ENVELOPES WITH OUR NAMES ON THEM!

AND OVER HERE -- WE GET TO WEAR *CLOAKS!*

THIS IS ALL JUST AN ELABORATE WAY FOR THEM TO TURN US INTO NERDS, ISN'T IT

THIS WAY

14 The Real Bonnie

171

I LOVE YOU TOO, STUART

BUT I --

I DON'T WANT ANYTHING TO CHANGE! I WANT MIMI TO STAY IN TOWN, FRAN TO STAY IN DERBY, PEOPLE TO STOP ASKING ME ABOUT MY CAREER PLANS . .

EVERYTHING NEEDS TO JUST *STOP!*

BONNIE - I'M NOT TALKING ABOUT THINGS *CHANGING* - NOTHING HAS TO CHANGE!

I WAS ENGAGED ONCE!

WH --

SORRY - BYE!

=SLAM=!

FRAN FACE

YEAH?

LET'S TALK ABOUT THE *DRAFT*

OHHH NO -- NOT THIS TIME, MIMI

EXCUSE ME?

NOPE! I'M NOT READY YET-- THIS TIME I'M GOING TO TAKE MY TIME, BUILD UP MY SKILLS

PLUS I CAN HELP GET ALL THE OTHER FRESHIES READY! I'M LIKE A *VETERAN* FRESHIE!

THAT'S AN OXYMORON

YOU'RE AN OXYMORON!

FRAN

I'M NOT TRYING OUT AND YOU CAN'T MAKE ME!

YOU WAIT TILL *BONNIE* HEARS ABOUT THIS, YOUNG LADY

WOW . . . I MEAN, IT'S BEEN FOREVER, BUT THAT WAS *AMAZING*

TELL ME ABOUT IT . . . JESUS

OH SHIT, WHAT **TIME** IS IT? I SHOULD GET GOING

NOOO NO

DON'T DO THAT -- COME ON, STAY

I DON'T KNOW . . .

MIMI, PLEASE SPEND THE NIGHT

I PROMISE TO KICK YOU OUT EARLY

I MEAN, YOU'VE COME ALL THIS WAY

DON'T YOU AT LEAST WANT TO **SEE** THE BEDROOM?

ᴇSIGHᴈ

I HAVEN'T HAD A BOYFRIEND, MUCH LESS A *DATE* IN THREE YEARS

AND HERE *SLAM* TURNS UP, HOT AND SMART AND NOT LOOKING FOR ANYTHING **SERIOUS** EITHER

I CAN'T BELIEVE HOW *LUCKY* I AM!

G'MAWNING STRANGE LADY!

AAAHH!

HEY SLAM!

HEY FRAN

WHAT ARE YOU DOING HERE SO EARLY?

PRACTICING. RICK -- THE RINK OWNER -- HAS BEEN LETTING ME COME IN EARLY

YOU KNOW... BEFORE I WAS A REF, I USED TO COACH -- DO YOU WANT ANY HELP?

OH, THANKS! BUT I ALREADY --

WHO LIK TO ROC THE PAR

FRAN LIKE TO ROCK THE PART

...HAVE BONNIE

HOW ARE YOU?

GOOD! YEAH

I HEARD YOUR DATE WENT WELL

REALLY? MIMI THOUGHT IT WENT WELL? BECAUSE SHE KIND OF RAN OUT...

...PRACTICALLY SCREAMING

PSH... SHE DOES THAT

SHE'LL BE TRAVELING FOR WORK FOR THE NEXT FEW WEEKS

SHE TRAVELS A LOT...

OH

OH

GOOD JOB FRAN, KEEPING THOSE KNEES BENT!

YOU LIKE HER, DON'T YOU?

YEAH... IF SHE'LL LET M

PAT PAT

STICK WITH IT, CHIEF

I KNOW HOW SHE FEELS

BALANCING WHAT SHE THINKS SHE WANTS WITH WHAT SHE ACTUALLY DOES

IT'S EXHAUSTING TRYING TO BE WHAT PEOPLE EXPECT OF YOU ALL THE TIME

WHO TOLD YOU YOU HAD TO BE THAT WAY?

YOUR BOYFRIEND?

STUART? NO WAY, THIS WAS MY EX. SHE HAD A WAY SHE WANTED ME TO BE, AND I LOVED HER AND DIDN'T WANT TO DISAPPOINT.

OBVIOUSLY THAT'S NOT IDEAL, BUT I DUNNO - IN THE END, BEING MYSELF JUST WRECKED THE RELATIONSHIP

SO WHY BOTHER?

BONNIE... SCREW THAT

JUST BRING IT

BE AS REAL AND WHATEVER AS YOU WANT TO BE

IF THEY'RE WORTHY, THEY'LL BE INTO IT

YEAH

UGH I NEED TO BE TALKING TO STUART ABOUT THIS STUFF

SOUNDS LIKE IT

I JUST WISH I WASN'T AFRAID HE'LL FLIP OUT JUST BECAUSE I WAS ONCE ENGAGED TO A WOMAN

WHY CAN I SAY THIS TO YOU AND NOT HIM?

HEH

RING RING

HELLO?

≶SIGH≷

SLAM, ARE YOU GONNA HIT ON ALL THE WOMEN IN THE LEAGUE?

NO! FRAN, I WASN'T--

YOU KNOW I'M GAY, RIGHT?

KEEP DOING LAPS, FRAN

I JUST DIDN'T WANT YOU TO WASTE THE EFFORT

HI, WHO'S . . . OH! HAROLD? OF COURSE I REMEMBER YOU

WHAT'S WRONG?

HERB'S *MISSING*? YEAH . . . OK, YEAH

I'LL BE RIGHT THERE!

SORRY GUYS, I GOTTA GO -- FRAN, WOULD YOU MIND IF SLAM HELPED YOU OUT TODAY?

IS EVERYTHING OKAY?

YEAH! I JUST -- BYE!

ALRIGHT FRAN LET'S SEE WHA YOU'VE GOT

AYE AYE CAP'N

WONDER TEAM ACTIVATE!

BONNIE? HI! WOW - THIS IS A SURPRISE

IT'S SO GOOD TO SEE YOU

I'VE BEEN WANTING TO TALK TO YOU ABOUT OUR LAST

NO TIME FOR THAT NOW!

WE HAVE A SUPER SERIOUS MISSION TO ATTEND TO

WHAT'S GOING ON?

HERB'S MISSING! I NEED TO FIND HIM, WANNA HELP?

OH!

SURE, OF COURSE -- I'LL GET MY COAT

GREAT! ON TO ASSEMBLE THE REST OF THE TEAM

TEAM?

CHERYL AND STEVE, OF COURSE!

WHO ELSE ARE WE--

COME ON!

AIT ...

WHY ARE YOU INVITING MY EX-ROOMMATE

AND THE GUY WHO HAS A CRUSH ON HER?

WE NEED STEVE BECAUSE HE KNOWS HOW TO TRACK BIGFOOTS

HERB'S A WEREWOLF

I'M SURE THE SAME PRINCIPLES APPLY

AND WE NEED *CHERYL* TO GET STEVE, SINCE HE LIKES HER

OH ...

IS THAT WHY YOU ASKED *ME?* TO GET CHERYL?

THAT AND I MISS YOUR CUTE FACE!

BONNIE ... CHERYL HATES *BOTH* OF US RIGHT NOW

I'M CONFIDENT THAT'S TEMPORARY

HI CHERYL!

WHAT THE F--

WE NEED YOUR HELP

FOR A SPECIAL MISSION

ARE YOU NUTS? I HATE BOTH OF YOU RIGHT NOW

I KNOW, BUT CHERYL -- IT'S BEEN A WHILE AND I WAS HOPING WE COULD BE *FRIENDS* AGAIN

FORGET IT

OKIE DOKE -- OFF TO STEVE'S HOUSE

YOU'LL NEVER GET STEVE WITHOUT ME

HE STILL LIKES WEREWOLVES, RIGHT?

⟨SIGH⟩ *FINE,* WAIT UP!

185

UM...

HI STEVE!

HELLO STEVE

CHERYL

LOOK, IF YOU GUYS ARE HERE TO ASK ME ON ANOTHER DOUBLE DATE...

I'M NOT REALLY INTERESTED IN PUTTING MYSELF THROUGH THAT AGAIN

HERB'S MISSING AND WE NEED YOUR PARTICULAR EXPERTISE

AND I BET CHERYL WANTS TO APOLOGIZE, TO BOOT!

WHAT?!

LET ME GRAB MY EQUIPMENT!

BONNIE! YOU BROUGHT ...AN ARMY

HI HAROLD

THIS IS KIND OF A *SENSITIVE* MATTER

AS HERB'S FRIEND, I CAN TRUST *YOU*, BUT...

DON'T WORRY, I CAN VOUCH FOR THEIR SILENCE

BESIDES, THE MORE HANDS ON DECK, THE EASIER TO FIND HIM, RIGHT?

≷SIGH≷ WELL IT'S JUST...IT'S HERB'S *LEAP MOON*

ONCE IN A WHILE HE, UM...HE...

...BECOMES HUMAN

≷GASP≷

HAROLD, HOW LONG DOES THIS NORMALLY LAST?

SOMETIMES A FEW DAYS

SOMETIMES ... WEEKS

WEEKS?!

AND YOU HAVE NO IDEA HOW TO TURN HIM BACK?

WOLFSBANE!

WHAT?

WOLFSBANE ... IT'S KIND OF LIKE A WEREWOLF ANTIDOTE

SO WE SHOULD FIND THE OPPOSITE OF THAT ...A HUMAN ANTIDOTE

BUT - WE DON'T WANT TO CURE HIM OF BEING A HUMAN FOREVER, RIGHT?

STUART, DON'T BE NAIVE

NO ONE LIKES BEING HUMAN

UGH, THIS IS HARD -- HAVE TO DO THE OPPOSITE OF ALL MY TRAINING!

WHAT'S SOMETHING THAT SUCKS FOR HUMANS BUT IS GREAT FOR WOLVES?

UH ... EATING HUMAN FLESH

HOWLING

WINTER

THE STARK FAMILY

HAHA - NICE ONE, CHERYL

THANKS

SO, UM ...

ARE YOU CAUGHT UP? WITH THE SHOW?

HEY, AT LEAST IT LOOKS LIKE BONNIE'S GETTING SOMEWHERE

YEAH, ONE OF BONNIE'S SUPERPOWERS IS MAKING FRIENDS

PLAID SHIRTS FOREVER!

≥PSH≤

I MEAN, WITH EVERYONE BUT CHERYL

HAROLD?

WHAT HAPPENED?

SHH, DON'T WORRY - LET'S GET YOU HOME

... OUT OF THESE GODFORSAKEN CLOTHES ...

HIGH FIVES!

THAT ... THAT WAS GREAT

STEVE ...

THERE'S NOTHING I NEED TO APOLOGIZE FOR, Y'KNOW

I WAS UP FRONT ABOUT WHAT THAT DATE WAS FROM THE BEGINNING

WELL, YOU MADE SURE I KNEW YOU HAD ZERO INTEREST IN ME, THAT'S FOR SURE

IT'S NOT THAT, I'VE JUST LIKED STUART FOR *SO* LONG ...

WELL, IF HE DOESN'T LIKE *YOU*, MAYBE IT'S TIME TO GET OVER HIM ALREADY

INSTEAD OF PISSING OFF THE PEOPLE YOU COULD ACTUALLY HAVE A RELATIONSHIP WITH

STUART...

SO THERE'S SOMETHING I WANT TO TELL YOU

WHAT?

YOU KNOW HOW I SAID I WAS... ENGAGED?

YEAH..

WHY, DO YOU STILL SEE HIM OR SOMETHING?

OH GOD, IT'S NOT THAT *SLAM* GUY, IS IT?

NO, I NEVER SEE HER

OH, OKAY. WAIT...

HER? YOU WERE ENGAGED... TO A... *WOMAN?*

YUP

OH MY GOD, FRAN WAS RIGHT - SHE *COULD* WHISK YOU OF TO *GAY CITY*...

WHA

DOES THAT... I MEAN DID YOU USED TO BE A... LESBIAN?

NO, I WAS -- I AM -- BI

WOW... I NEVER THOUGHT THAT WAS LIKE, AN ACTUAL *THING*

WHAT! OF COURSE IT'S A THING, SILLY!

SO DOES THAT MEAN THAT YOU WANT TO DATE *GIRLS* AGAIN?

OR... UM ... ALSO?

NO! IT JUST MEANS I LIKE *PEOPLE* --

-- NOT THEIR GENDER

ISN'T IT NICE KNOW THAT I'D LIKE YO JUST AS MUCH IF Y HAD LADY BITS?

UM

... shutup and skate! We'll see all you cats and kittens in the next book!

me at 2ND tryouts!

first bout!

full crop of fresh meat

official league portrait as a new freshie

MY DERBY SCRAPBOOK!

only picture where I'm actually low enough

Monica Gallagher

first team shirt!

me & derby wifey, Roxy Balboa!

BONNIE SKETCHBOOK

FIRST TIME I EVER DREW BONNIE! ON A NOTEBOOK, WHILE IN A MEETING AT MY DAY JOB. MEMORIES!

BONNIE SKETCHBOOK

BONNIE WITH HER YOUNGER SELF

FIRST PROTOTYPE DRAWING OF SLAM!

IPHONE WALLPAPERS I COBBLED TOGETHER A FEW YEARS BACK

SUPER EARLY POSTER IDEA

SOME OF MY CRAZY-PERSON STORY NOTES

TATTOO LOVE!

TATTOOS ARE A BIG PART OF DERBY AND SOMETHING I HOLD VERY DEAR, SO HERE'S A COMPILATION OF SOME OF THE TATTOOS I'VE DRAWN INTO THE SERIES! (SOME CHANGE A LOT, SOME DISAPPEAR AT RANDOM, IT'S A THING!)

MY REFERENCE MAP FOR SLAM'S TATTOOS, SINCE HE HAS BY FAR THE *MOST!*

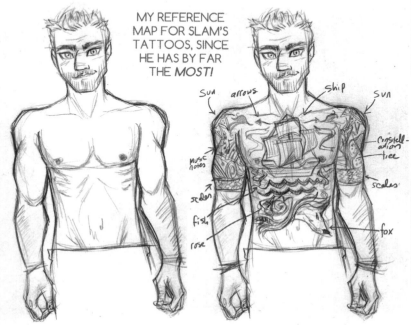

MIMI STARTED OUT WITH AN ELEPHANT ON HER ARM

WHICH EVOLVED INTO A PHOENIX!

BONNIE HAS ONE HEART TATTOO ON EACH ARM (SHE WEARS HER HEART ON HER SLEEVES, HAR HARR)

MOST OF THE RANDOM TATTOOS I DRAW SEEM TO INVOLVE LOTS OF SWIRLS

JUUUUST INDETERMINABLE SWIRLS!

HATTIE HELLFIRE HAS FLAMES ON HER UPPER LEFT ARM

(THE 666 IS HER TEAM NUMBER THAT SHE DRAWS ON FOR BOUTS)

LORELEI GETMORE HAS STARS RIGHT BELOW HER COLLARBONE

AGRO AMELIA HAS A BOUQUET OF FLOWERS ON HER RIGHT ARM

(WHICH DIVERGES FROM HER SOUR PERSONALITY)

THUMBNAILING

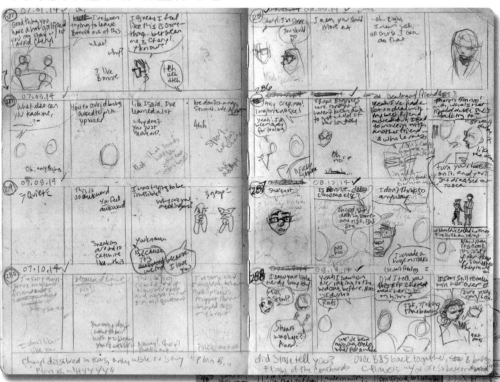

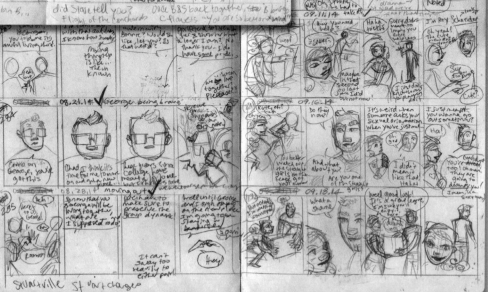

I PLOT OUT MY STRIPS IN LITTLE FOUR-SQUARE PANELS ON PAGES OF MY 5" X 8" SKETCHBOOK, WHERE IF I'M *NOT* DOING A GOOD JOB PLANNING, THEY LOOK SORT OF VACANT AND TEXT-ONLY AS SHOWN HERE

THIS IS AN EXAMPLE OF WHEN I'M PAYING MORE ATTENTION AND DOING A BETTER JOB PLANNING. HOWEVER, SOMETIMES WHEN I SKETCH A LOT INITIALLY I FALL IN LOVE WITH THE FIRST VERSION OF THAT PANEL AND CAN NEVER RECREATE IT IN THE STRIP ITSELF. HURGH!

Process for Each Strip!

I start off with thumbnails, super rough and scratchy, in my 5" x 8" sketchbook. I've ruled out with the four panels, strip number, and date.

Next, I pencil in the strip on 11" x 17" Bristol board with blue lead, and ink with a Pentel Brush pen.

I put in the word bubbles for guidance - I only ink them in when I prep the original for selling.

Ewwww, scanner shadows - the WORST! I have to get rid of these guys after I scan my Bristol board in two pieces

In Photoshop, I use some actions (auto contrast, adjust hue/saturation, set layer to multiply) to get rid of the blues and bring out the inks more.

Also, I replace my hand lettering with a font I made OF my handwriting!

And VOILA! Yer finished strip, ready for posting!

BIG SHOUTOUT

To all my Kickstarter Backers, without whom this book wouldn't be possible!

T. Perran Mitchell

The most holy and exalted Reverend Rafer Roberts, demon slayer

Michael R. Underwood

Kata Kane

Robert E. Stutts

Andy loves Jenny Perez

Byers Remorse

Mr. Phil Jackson

Pop Rox

Em Dash

Katrina Heiser

Zoomintroll

Ben Grisanti

Erin Hawley

Marcie Pry aka Short Temper, Hellions of Troy Roller Derby

Calvin Roberts

Kadie Yale

JD Kirk

Cosmo

Suzy Creamcheese

Michael Bracco

Daniel Buck

Robert Gonzo Wicker

Julie L Spradley

Kate N.

Gabriel Schlesinger

Jim Dougan

Michael Luhinec

Lauren M Pedestrian

Jim Otermat

Matiukas

Jill

Hillary Froemel

Ryan Gallagher & Sarah Ly

Scott Early

Doom Buggy

D.J. Trindle

Big Al Sparrow

Alex Lyle

Jon Parrish

Darryl Warcup

Mel T.

Ed and Teri Moore

Alicia Mundinger

Hal and the CCRG Junkyard Dolls!

Guy Edwards

Firefighter Fawn Colonbatto

Kofi Jamal Simmons

Isaac "Will It Work" Dansicker

Brenna Painter

Kellyn (Jean Rot 'n Bury #1966)

Barbara R Leyhe

Kristin Maun

Ryan Dunlavey

Marissa Frattini

Aabra & Matt

Evette Langford

Stephen Perkins

Amalia Helene Menna

Sheilah Villari

Henriikka Julkunen

Erin Jameson

David Kinsel

Kathy Hadfield

Henry Roll-ins

ben hengst

Shield Bonnichsen

Ed Mathews

KN

captain awesome

Madeline Galac aka Bunsen Burn Her

Kat Lombard-Cook

Imrie-Brownes

Marci McCann

David Lizewski

The Talented Mr. Whipley

Shanna Broussard

Captain SlamHer

Victor Von Thoom

Meghan Euringer

Dash V Danya (NOVA Roller Derby)

AMBUSH

Celestial Awesome One

Thomas Zimmermann

Philip "Apoctimus Prime" Messina

Luc de Chancenotte

Lindsey Gerstlauer

Kelly Taylor

Nicole "Panda Scare" DeCuir

PJ Hambrick

The Helsing Family

Emily and Ann

Brent Stringer

Shylo

Dan Hould

Braver Cruz Montero

Philip Lopez

Bob

H Lynnea Johnson

Jo Wood

Jon Eaton

Josh & Lani Paulik

Aunt Louise & Uncle Mike

marybeth manarchy

Andy Haigh @Wolverinesclaws

Battlestar Galactikate

Irish Frisky

Jeb Korzilius

Corinne "Cringe" Costello

GriffinFire

Eric V.

Joel Kovach

James Mendez

Jonathan Edwards

Greg Lockard

Katalyn Ford

Alias Majere

Mikey

Lalirem Slimmers

Amy Jo "Bitches Bruze" Moore

Kacey Huntington (I.M. Pain)

Athena "Colada" Caran

bleuh moon

Grand Theft Autumn

CHUCK STEAK

dixie ross

JEFF SUON

Emily Beauparlant

Amanda Raifsnider

Dan Theodore

Christian Sager

John S. Troutman

Castle K

Dave Carter

Caitlin Jane Hughes

Reckless

Elizabeth Williamson

Jacob

Tony Allegro

Cindy Womack

Mike "Tanukitsune" Alonso

peter rabbid

Matt Benter

Sam Perkins

Ilona Rossman Ho

Farmer's Slaughter

Heather

The Shwilliams Family

Scott Wilke

Jamie Tanner

Josh Coale

Jamie S. Rich

Margreet de Heer

Per Sjödén

Alik Naomi Seropian

Rev. Dr. Miss Danielle Q. Corsetto III, Ph.D

Amy Chu

M Alia Denny

Abby VanderWall

Ben Maloney

Ehma G

splendidgeek

Emma Levine

Smashingsuns

Jesse Post

Mario Candelaria

Wolfsbanel

Chris Murrin

Hoyt Heaton

John MacLeod

Mike Dawson runningflatnovel.com

Chris Rosa

Andrea Demonakos

Mike Riley

Markus Magnitz

Janie Sacco

Shawn Atkins

Hannah May Reynolds

Gabi's Olympic Cards & Comics

Thomas Jansen

Alicia McCoy

Amber Wade

Ann "Fubarella" Sullivan

Jade Miller

Caley Ross

Kira Mandel

Oni Press

A. J. Stimel

Uhura Jones

Lennhoff Family

SCG

Lara Duncan

Buck Hockey

Stephanie Byrd

Ruth Angelici

Batty Oracle - CCRD

Ryan John

Ksenia Winnick

Steve & Alison Gallagher

Kyla Blythe

Don Bailey

Daniel Govar

Sara Bookoit

Chris

Joseph Schmidt

Dan Faust

Linnea Covington

Acacia Sears

Anthony Angell

Erin 'Sharon Diseases' Brown

Ora McWilliams (Paranoid Parrot)

R. BRIAN LONG

Angel H.

Allie B. Back

Emily Agueda

Sadie Stingray

Hannah Sanford

Selena Grinham

Jolene "Bob" Taylor